BATTLE BOOKS

MARATHON

Gary Smailes

Illustrated by Ollie Cuthbertson

For Poppy — G.S.

First published in 2011
by Franklin Watts

Text © Gary Smailes 2011
Illustrations by Ollie Cuthbertson © Franklin Watts 2011
Cover design by Jonathan Hair

Franklin Watts
338 Euston Road
London NW1 3BH

Franklin Watts Australia
Level 17/207 Kent Street
Sydney, NSW 2000

A CIP catalogue record for this book
is available from the British Library.

ISBN: 978 1 4451 0114 9

1 3 5 7 9 10 8 6 4 2

Printed in Great Britain

Franklin Watts is a division of Hachette Children's Books,
an Hachette UK company.
www.hachette.co.uk

"When I went to school my history lessons were all about learning the names of kings and endless lists of dates. *Yawn*. But exciting history asks: How did people live and how did they die? How did they feel? Were they just like us or more like aliens from another planet? Those are the questions that *Battle Books* explore. I wish Gary Smailes and his books had been around when I went to school."
— **Terry Deary, author of** *Horrible Histories*

BATTLE BOOKS

Prepare to fight your own battle...

Start the story, then choose which numbered paragraph to follow. Go to that paragraph to continue on and see if you can gain a "great general ranking" and defeat the Persians at the Battle of Marathon!

Miltiades the Younger

This is YOU – the leader of an army of warriors from the great city of Athens. Though you are 60 years old, you are one of the few Athenians to have fought against the Persians, and that is why you have been chosen to help defend Athens against the Persians on the plain of Marathon.

◊ City state: Athens
◊ Fighting ability: Superb
◊ Armour: Bronze breastplate and shield

◊ Troop type: Infantry
◊ Favourite weapon: Spear

YOUR LEADERS

Polemarch Callimachus

Callimachus is an Athenian tribal leader. He holds the position of Polemarch, one of the most senior positions in society. His role is both a military one and a spiritual one. He is highly experienced in battle, and a fierce fighter. But he is also a deeply respected commander.

◊ City state: Athens
◊ Troop type: Infantry
◊ Fighting ability: Superb
◊ Favourite weapon: Spear
◊ Armour: Bronze breastplate and round, bronze-plated shield

Leontis

Leontis is a tribal leader and a close friend of Miltiades. He is a huge man, built like a hero of legend, and a highly skilled warrior. He is a influential leader and a great inspiration to his men.

◊ City state: Athens
◊ Troop type: Infantry
◊ Fighting ability: Superb
◊ Favourite weapon: Spear
◊ Armour: Bronze breastplate and round, bronze-plated shield

YOUR WARRIORS

Hoplites

You command just one type of warrior, the hoplite. These are citizens of Athens who are trained to fight. They are armed with a heavy bronze breastplate, bronze greaves on the front of their legs and a huge round wooden shield, covered with a thin layer of bronze. On their heads they wear a bronze helmet. Though hoplites carry a sword, their main weapon is a long wooden spear. Hoplites can fight on their own or in a formation known as a phalanx.

Arimnestos

Arimnestos is leader of the Plataeans, from the Greek city of Plataea. He has brought 1,000 warriors to help the Athenians. He is a young, brave and spirited fighter. But he is also a calm, intelligent leader.

◊ City state: Plataea
◊ Troop type: Infantry
◊ Fighting ability: Excellent
◊ Favourite weapon: Sword
◊ Armour: Shield and breastplate

FIGHTING FORMATION

The phalanx

This formation is made by ranks of hoplites lined up close together. Each man in the front rank locks his shield with the man to his left and right, forming a great shield wall. The next rank of warriors pushes up close, and thrusts their spears over the shoulders of the men in the ranks in front. A third rank is then added. It is common for the Athenians to fight with eight ranks.

PERSIAN ARMY

Legend and myth

The Persian army is greatly feared by the Greeks, some even believe that they are not human, such is their reputation in battle. The Persians prefer to fight with the support of horsemen (cavalry). They also have archers available, as well as the troops below.

PERSIAN TROOPS

Spear men

These warriors form most of the Persian army. They are lightly armoured, but this means they are very agile and can move quickly. They can fight on their own, or in a formation called a shield wall. Most are not professional soldiers, and are not as highly trained or skilled as the feared Immortals (see below).
◊ Country: Persia
◊ Troop type: Light infantry
◊ Fighting ability: Average
◊ Favourite weapon: Spear
◊ Armour: Wicker shield

Immortals

These are the elite warriors of the Persian army. They are highly skilled, using a spear or short sword. Their clothing is brightly coloured and they often wear a cloth hat that can be pulled over their faces.
◊ Country: Persia
◊ Troop type: Heavy infantry
◊ Fighting ability: Superb
◊ Favourite weapon: Spear
◊ Armour: Scalemail and shield

In 490 BCE, when the Persian army landed on the coast of Greece, the city of Athens was thrown into chaos.

As a young man you, Miltiades the Younger, actually fought on the side of the Persians in a war against the Scythians. But soon after you joined a revolt and escaped to Athens. Athenians were suspicious of your past, though, and you quickly made many enemies. These were powerful men, and you were placed on a false trial and sentenced to death.

However, with the arrival of the Persian threat, you were released from prison. The city council debated what to do, and in the discussion that followed you argued that Athenians must rise to arms and march to meet the Persians. Many councillors thought you might be mad – or worse, a traitor – but when the vote was taken it was decided to fight!

Ten great tribes of Athenian hoplites have been formed, each of about 1,000 warriors. Since you have experience of fighting the Persians, you are in charge of one of these tribes. The mass of warriors has blocked the Persian exits from the beach under the guidance of the Polemarch Callimachus. Here you met up with a further 1,000 hoplites from Plataea, all eager to join the fight against the Persians. The Spartans have also promised to come to the battle.

But since then days have passed and little has happened. Both armies sit facing each other across the plain of Marathon. Athenian tradition means that with each new day the command of the army passes to a different tribe leader. So far, each leader has been unwilling to fight. So you waited, and when the sun rose on your day of command, you knew that blood would flow.

Your Athenian army is ready to do battle! Prepare to prove to the citizens of Athens and Ares, the god of war, that you are truly an Athenian worthy of great honour.

◊ *Go to section 1.*

POSITIONS AT THE START OF THE BATTLE OF MARATHON

1 You stand in the warming morning sun, leaning against an olive tree. Your old legs are stiff from last night's sleep.

Across the open valley you can see the massive Persian army. People expected a quick battle but the gods had other ideas. Knowing the Persians had horse-mounted warriors – cavalry – the Athenian leaders positioned their warriors amongst the olive trees, where it would be difficult to ride a horse. As a result, the Persians refused to fight. That was until command fell to you.

Standing with you in the olive grove are the other nine Athenian commanders, Arimnestos, leader of the Plataeans, and the Polemarch Callimachus.

"We have had word that last night the Persians loaded their cavalry onto their ships," says Callimachus, his white beard standing proud against his tanned, leathery skin. "We think they plan to sail along the coast to Athens. The omens are on our side. This morning, the entrails of the sacrificed goats were clean and free of stink, a sure sign that the gods are with us. What do you intend to do, Miltiades?"

◊ *If you wish to prepare the Athenian army to attack, go to 90.*
◊ *If you wish to wait, go to 80.*

2   Your joints may already ache with the strain of
combat, but you're not done yet. You adjust the
position of your shield, so its weight is evenly
spread, and wipe the sweat from your right hand to
grasp your spear firmly. Then you push forward.

The fact you ordered a large number of warriors
into the centre means the battle is cramped. Just
ahead of you, the phalanx is eight men deep and
holding firm. The back ranks are out of spear range
and are focusing on pushing. You squeeze past
these men towards the front ranks.

As you push into the front rank, the tip of a
Persian spear thrusts towards your face. It has
been pushed over the top of the rank in front. You
try to move backwards, but the spear tip squeezes
through the slit in your helmet and into your eye.
You hear a pop and pain fills your head. Your
legs collapse and you crash down onto the blood-
soaked earth.

◊   *You are dead – the Battle of Marathon is over for
you. Go to 61 to discover your fate.*

---

3   You watch helplessly as the man fights for his
life. Persian warriors have surrounded him and
he is trying to hold them off with his shield. The
Athenian line is now about ten paces away. They
are desperately trying to stay in formation and no
one is moving forward to help the man.

As you watch the fight unfold, you notice a shape bobbing around behind the Persian warriors. As you stare, the shapes flits closer and then appears just a few paces away. It is a Persian archer, dressed in bright red clothes, with yellow material covering his face. Before you can react the man shoots an arrow in your direction. He has been hunting you.

You try to lift your shield, but the archer is close and his shot is accurate. The arrow flies over the top of your shield and thuds into your exposed neck. You grasp the wooden shaft, which now protrudes from just below your chin. You try to scream, but your vocal cords have been sliced and no sound emerges, instead bloody foam froths from your mouth as you struggle for breath before collapsing to the ground.

◊ *You are dead – the Battle of Marathon is over for you. Go to 61 to discover your fate.*

---

4 As you gaze on at the two lines of fighting warriors, the shriek of a bird attracts your attention. You shield your eyes from the sun as you gaze into the sky above the battle.

A soaring eagle dips and dives high above you. In the eagle's talons is a monstrous blood-red snake, alive and still struggling. As you watch, the snake twists in the bird's claws, moving its head backwards towards the eagle. The snake's fangs lash out, snapping at the bird, which drops the snake in shock. You watch as the blood-red snake plummets to the ground, disappearing into the mass of fighting warriors.

This is clearly a sign – an omen – from the gods.

◊ *If the gods are telling you to attack, go to 98.*

◊ *If the gods wish you to retreat, go to 24.*

5   After the initial flurry of courage, the phalanx has once again stopped advancing. Both sides continue to push; both sides continue to thrust, poke and slash; both sides continue to die and fight in the heat and dust.

◊ *If you wish to try to inspire your men again, go to 33.*

◊ *If you feel that your men will never ever win, order the retreat at 76.*

6   You move through the ranks of your warriors and take up a position in the centre of the army. The flutes to the rear toot out a blast and your warriors move forward as one. Across the flat, dusty ground ahead you can see the enemy – a line of spear-wielding warriors, most of who are dressed in black and white, with their black-and-white wicker shields forming an impressive wall.

As you close in on the Persian line you start to see a number of different warriors pushing their way past the black-and-white wicker shields and into the space between the two armies. These are dressed in red and yellow uniforms, and are armed with bows. They start to shoot in your direction and a screen of arrows arcs high into the air before falling onto your warriors. As the phalanx slowly moves forward the number of arrows increases until men are dying to your left and right. You can feel the panic building in the Athenian ranks.

◊ *If you wish to order the retreat from the deadly arrows, go to 38.*

◊ *If you wish to order your troops to break formation and sprint forward to attack the Persians, go to 41.*

Years of battle experience have taught you that when an enemy turns its back, it is time for the slaughter to begin! With a twinkle in your eye and blood lust rising in your stomach, you scream for your men to attack. The desire to kill fills you and you spring forward. Your shield bobs and bangs as you run, and the pain of your old elbow wound flashes up your arm. You adjust your grip on your spear.

Suddenly you are amongst the fleeing Persians. You see their exposed backs as they race away. A man is close by; you prepare to strike but he stumbles and rolls past you. Ahead you see another exposed back. You pump your legs and are soon next to the man.

◊ *If you wish to let the Persian escape, go to 19.*

◊ *If you wish to attack the Persian, go to 57.*

8 The sun is sinking in the sky as the day draws on, but it is still hot. The phalanx in front of you is clearly tiring. It has now been engaged for more than an hour, and your men will not be able to take much more.

You decide that you must help hold back the Persians. You lift your spear and push through the ranks. You force your way to the third rank and position your shield so it rests on the back of the man in front, giving him support.

Suddenly pressure increases on your shield as the front ranks push backwards. Something is very wrong. You brace your feet to try to hold the line when the man in front suddenly falls. He tumbles under your feet, his face covered in blood. When you look up a Persian is standing in front of you!

The line has split and the Persians have broken through. You struggle to bring your spear down, but it is trapped in the plumes and helmets of the men in front. You drop your weapon and go for your sword. The Persian, carrying a curved blade, lunges forward and rakes his blade across your face. The metal nicks your neck. Your lifeblood spurts in a fountain, covering your attacker. Power goes from your legs; life slips from your body.

◊ *You have been killed in battle. Go to 61 to discover your fate.*

Stepping forward you shout to four Athenian warriors close by to follow you. After just ten paces you are behind your tight hoplite line. You don't wait for the men to part and let you pass. Instead you lift your sandalled foot and kick hard at the man in front. He flinches, moving slightly to the side and you squeeze past. Suddenly you are out the other side and surrounded by Persians. You look to the left and right, and are relieved to see the four Athenian warriors close by.

The stranded warrior is directly in front of you, still lying exposed on the floor. You rush forward, jumping over him and pushing the shocked Persians backwards.

The man is now safely behind you and instinctively the four Athenian warriors come to help. You move closer to the Athenian on your left, protecting his body with your shield. The man to your left does the same, and his shield moves to protect your body. The mini shield wall does its job, pushing the Persians back and giving the man behind you time to scramble to his feet. You wait until he has reached the safety of the Athenian line, then edge backwards.

Your actions have saved the stranded warrior, but your old body is suffering. Your muscles ache; the elbow of your shield arm is stiff and hurts whenever you move. Sweat covers your body. As you slowly recover you see a messenger pushing his way through the crowd towards you. You suspect he brings news of the battle on the wings.
◊ *Go to 47.*

---

10 From your position at the back of the phalanx it is impossible to see anything other than the battle immediately ahead of you. You start to walk to the right, skirting along the back ranks of the fighting Athenians, shouting encouraging words as you walk in the hot sun. As you reach the end of the huge block of warriors you come to a more open area of the plain. The sea is now very close and you can hear the waves crashing against the shore. Ahead of you fighting is still taking place, but rather than a large phalanx, Athenian warriors

scrap with the Persians in small packs.

Just then, a group of three enemy warriors appear a few paces ahead of you. Two of them are immediately attacked by Athenians, but the third sprints towards you. His spear is held above his head and he thrusts it down at you. You must dive out of the way, but which way will you roll?

◊ *To roll to the right, go to 96.*
◊ *To roll to the left, go to 45.*

11 The phalanx is a mighty formation, but once it is moving you have almost no control over it. You accept that you will be marching through the cloud of arrows. You adjust your position so you are once again in the front rank and, dipping your helmet slightly and shutting your eyes, you stride forward towards the Persians. You pray to the gods to keep you safe.

The phalanx pulls you forward, and as you close in on the Persian line, the arrows begin to stop falling. You open your eyes to see the black-and-white wicker shields of the Persians warriors just a spear thrust away. They are lined up in a wall formation. Your shield smashes into the shield of a bearded Persian, knocking the wind from you. You are too close to strike him with your spear and instead you aim for the man behind.

At that exact moment, the Persians push forward, forcing you to step back and causing you to lose your balance. Before the bearded Persian can attack, you feel rough hands on your shoulders, pulling you backwards through the ranks to safety.

The Persians and Athenians have locked shields and the line is holding firm. The battle has dissolved into a pushing match, but it looks as though the Persians may be winning.

◊ *To push your way back into the fight, go to 2.*
◊ *To wait a moment to see what happens, go to 34.*

Blood pumps like liquid fire through your veins as you rush forward. Within a few steps you are at the Athenian line. Your men step aside to let you into the line and you slip into place, thrusting your shield into position. It feels good to complete the wall, protecting the man to your left.

The Persians are within touching distance and they push back on your shield. They are so close that you can smell their bodies, but despite the squeeze, you manoeuvre your spear over the wall, into the mass of the enemy ahead. You desperately

thrust and jab with your lethal spear tip, but with little control. You feel it hitting flesh and bone; screams rise up but you can't see your victims. The enemy are a blur of black and white, clothes and shields all with the same design. You shout encouragement to the men about you, urging them to step forward and push back the Persians.

The Athenian line reacts and as one the warriors push. The sudden forward movement of the shields shocks the enemy, and for a split second they step backward. This leaves a space between the lines. Sweat pours down your face and you pant like the old man you are.

◊ *If you wish to seize the moment and step forward into the gap between the lines like one of Homer's heroes, go to 56.*

◊ *If you wish to keep your position, go to 91.*

Rating: OK General

You are not a poor general – so it could be worse – but you really need to try harder. You have done well to get this far, and displayed feats of bravery. But some of your choices have been poor, and you failed to stand up to the Persians when it really mattered. You must have more faith in the strength and skill of your warriors, and not be afraid to keep pushing at the Persian line.

You may be an old man, but you are never too old to learn from your mistakes. You still have the potential to be a great general.

◊ *Go now to 1 and prove you have what it takes to save Athens from the Persian invaders, and become a great Athenian general.*

14 You feel retreat is dishonourable, but to remain alone so close to the Persians would mean certain death. So you turn your back on the enemy line and jog back towards the Athenians. Pride fills your heart as you see the line of bronze shields, holding firm as the Persians push hard, spears thrusting and biting.

You spot a small section of the line that has no Persians close by, and head in that direction. The line opens as you near and you slip through. You are unable to look your fellow Athenians in the eyes as you rest. Your legs ache and your left elbow is burning. Age is catching up on you!

As you recover, you see a messenger approaching through the crowd behind the battle line.

◊ *To find out what news he brings, go to 47.*
◊ *To ignore the messenger, go to 72.*

15 You gaze on with pride as thousands of heavily armoured Athenian warriors march into position.

You move into the centre of your army. To your right and left you see the hoplites formed into neat lines. You pass the word to advance and a shrill toot echoes from a nearby horn. In response, your hoplites start to walk forward slowly, forming a mass of tightly packed men, their shields producing a glittering wall of bronze.

As you pace forward the fennel bushes that sprout from the dusty soil snap and scratch at your legs. After a few paces you see a line of Persians scurry out in front of their army. They are archers who begin to shoot swarms of arrows at your hoplites once they are in range. The arrows plunge down onto the heads of your men.

◊ *To continue your slow advance through the deadly arrow storm, go to 49.*

◊ *To issue the order to charge forward, even though it will break up the rigid formation, go to 28.*

---

16 Leontis moves to your side and rests his hand on your shoulder to stop you.

"Watch, old man," he says.

You do as he suggests, simply watching the Athenians. What you see makes you proud to be part of the great city. They tighten their line, moving closer to each other, creating an solid wall of shields. The men in the back ranks brace themselves, heaving back against the weight of the Persians. After a few minutes they halt the Persian push.

Time is passing. You glance to the right, but the light reflecting off the sea makes it difficult to find the Plataeans. You look to your left, but the plain drops into a slight hollow and you are unable to see past the fighting men.

You turn your attention to the line ahead of you and fear grips your stomach as you see the Persians once again pushing the Athenians back. Your warriors fight hard, but they are giving ground on the dusty, fennel covered plain.

◊ *If you wish to rush bravely into the fight to inspire your men, go to 12.*

◊ *If you trust your men to hold the line, go to 74.*

You adjust your shield before forcing your way towards the Polemarch. Your left elbow is burning with pain. Finally, you stand at Callimachus's side. He glances at you and smiles.

Then the Persians are on you both, attacking from all directions. For a few minutes you thrust, parry and block with your shield to fend them off. Then the battle seems to pause. You watch in horror as an Immortal warrior appears to the rear of Callimachus and plunges a spear into his unprotected back. The spear tip pops out through his chest.

The shriek that emerges from Callimachus's lips freezes the Immortals who surround him. They step backwards and watch. The Polemarch drops his shield and spear, and then grips the tip of the Persian spear with both hands. Using all his strength he pulls the spear away from him, feeding the blood-stained shaft through his own body. He continues to pull, hand over hand, until the spear is free of his chest. Callimachus holds the spear aloft. He turns in your direction, a smile on his face, before he is finally overcome and falls to the ground.

As you watch, a blade strikes your helmet – the clang causing your ears to ring. A second blade smashes into your chest and you topple backwards. In your final moments, you see the shape of a huge bird of prey circling high above the battle against the blue sky.

◊ *You have been killed in battle. Go to 13 to discover your fate.*

You and your men continue forward in formation.
Sweat drips down from your forehead and stings
your eyes. The roar of the battle is softened by
your metal helmet, but all around you see carnage.

With each step another hoplite is hit by arrows.
It is not long before you lose count of the number
of men who slump to the ground.

The arrows keep coming and you lift your
shield to try to give yourself some protection.
You then look up into the sky. At first you see just
blueness – no clouds – then the large tip of an
arrow seems to hover just above you. It plunges
down and enters your helmet through the narrow
eye slit and does not stop. The last thing you see
is a bright white flash as the metal tip buries itself
deep into your brain.

◊ *You have been killed in battle. Turn to 61 to discover
your fate.*

Your spear is poised, ready to strike as the Persian
sprints just a few paces ahead of you. Yet, you are
unable to kill the man. Though his back is exposed,
you decide to let him live. You slow down,
lowering your spear, and let him slip away.

The Persians are now flooding towards the
beach and the safety of their ships. You follow the
crowd, making your way across the dusty ground
which leads to the sandy beach.

Looking up you see the Persians have formed a thin semicircle of warriors. This line of men protects the Persians behind, who are trying desperately to get into their ships. Already a number of vessels have cast off into the bay.

Suddenly you hear a familiar voice cry out. To your right you can see Callimachus the Polemarch, the spiritual leader of your army. He has been isolated and is surrounded by a group of Persians. They are dressed in the shocking bright yellow and purple gowns of the feared Immortal guards. They circle around the Polemarch like hungry mountain lions, waiting for the moment to pounce. His death is imminent.

◊ *If you wish to risk your life to save Callimachus, go to 32.*

◊ *However, if you feel Callimachus is already doomed, then move towards the Persian ships by going to 87.*

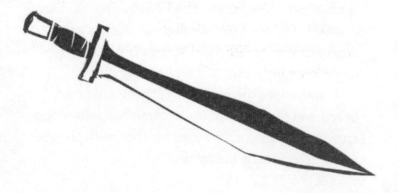

You realise now that your decision to strengthen the centre was a mistake. You pass the order to the leaders of the tribes for every third warrior from the back four ranks to come out of combat and move immediately to the right wing.

It takes a few minutes, and you watch in silence as the hoplites extract themselves from the phalanx and form up in a loose group behind the fighting. The ground is rough here, with fennel bushes and small dried streambeds making the ground uneven. However, the group of warriors form themselves into a small formidable block, and set off to the right.

When you turn your attention to the centre your heart sinks. The central phalanx has been weakened by your removing men and they have started to give ground. The Persians are proving too strong for the Athenians, and even as you watch you can see the phalanx retreating pace by pace.

◊ *If you feel the phalanx will not hold and wish to order the retreat now, go to 50.*

◊ *If you wish to keep fighting and pray the centre will hold, go to 31.*

You have fought in enough battles to know that victory rests in the hands of the gods. You therefore decide to wait, and let the fighting continue.

You push forward until you are standing just behind the first rank of your phalanx. The black-and-white clad Persian spear men push their wicker shields up against bronze Athenian shields.

Your attention is drawn away from the main line to a small skirmish that has developed to your left. A handful of Persians have tried to force their way around the side of the phalanx, and a group of Athenians are battling to stop their progress. This is not unusual, but in the crowd there is a huge Athenian warrior struggling towards the scrap with a massive boulder lifted over his head. He staggers forward, then launches the boulder at the nearest Persian. The mighty rock strikes the enemy warrior, sending him spinning to the ground. Seconds later hoplite blades finish him off.

The main battle in the centre continues. The two shield walls remain pushed together. However, the lines are now evenly matched and the battle is left once again in the hands of the gods.

◊ *If you wish to end the battle and order the retreat, go to 25.*

◊ *If you wish to let your men fight on, go to 4.*

You start to organise a fighting retreat. You pass the word to the hoplites close by to come to you, and then move about twenty paces from the main phalanx. The word spreads like wildfire and men start to dip away from the centre. This is weakening the formation and you know that you have little time left before it collapses and the Persians flood through.

You have collected a few hundred warriors and now is the time to escape.

◊ *If you wish to fight your way back to the olive groves, go to 73.*
◊ *If you wish to head inland through the marshes to the safety of the mountains, go to 62.*

23 You leave the Polemarch to his fate – guilt and cowardice hanging over you. The fighting around you eases and you can now see ocean to your right. You head for the Persian ships.

As you near the beach the fennel-covered ground gives way to sand. The Persians have formed a line of warriors that arcs across the beach. Behind the line, the Persians clamber onto their ship in safety, whilst their comrades in the line fight and die to protect them. As the minutes, then hours pass by, you watch helplessly as boat after boat fills with Persians, then slips away.

As the number of Persians on the beach dwindles your army gains control. They capture or kill the remaining Persians, but are unable to stop the last few ships escaping.

It is now mid-afternoon and you must decide what to do next.

◊ *If you wish to race in the hot afternoon sun across the mountains to try to defend Athens from a possible Persian attack, go to 78.*

◊ *If you wish to remain on the battlefield, make a sacrifice to the gods and bury your dead, go to 100.*

24 The cunning snake plummeting to its death is a clear sign from the gods that if you carry on with this battle you will also fall to your death.

Without hesitation you run madly to the head

of the phalanx. You push through the tightly packed men, screaming that they must retreat. Leontis appears at your arm. His face is blood spattered and worried. You tell him of the eagle and the snake, and the fact that this must be a sign of defeat. He thinks for a moment then agrees, solemnly shaking his head.

The two of you begin to pass the order to retreat and within minutes the front ranks of the phalanx break away. The black-and-white clad Persians surge forward.

You are still trying to direct the retreat when death arrives. In a flash, a spear tip pierces your neck, followed by a gush of blood. Your final thought, as darkness arrives, is that it looks very much like the blood-red snake.

◊ *You have been killed in battle. Turn to 13 to discover your fate.*

You begin to panic as a feeling of dread floods through your body. You must order your men to retreat! You see in your mind a blood-soaked plain, fennel bushes squashed by the bodies of Athenian warriors. In the distance you can see the sky glowing orange as Athens burns. You suddenly realise that the gods wish for a Persian victory.

You race through the crowd of Athenian warriors, shouting that they are doomed. Many of the men you pass simply stop and stare. Suddenly a firm hand grabs your left arm, and pain jolts through your body.

"What ails you?" asks Leontis, holding you tightly. You try to explain that the battle will end in defeat and that Athenian blood will run red into the sea. He smiles calmly and pulls you away from the battle. It seems your part in the Battle of Marathon is over.

◊ *You are a disgrace to Athens. Turn to 61 to discover what the gods have in store for you.*

You are now a few paces behind the front line. You
remove your helmet and wipe sweat from your
eyes with the back of your hand. You glance at the
top of the helmet. The once magnificent purple
horsehair plume is now nothing more than a mass
of blood-stained bristles. With a smile you replace
your helmet.

The shriek of a bird attracts your attention.
Shielding your eyes from the sun, you gaze into
the sky. A soaring eagle has a writhing, blood-red
snake in its talons. As you watch, the snake twists
in the bird's claws, moving its head backwards
towards the breast of the eagle. The snake's fangs
lash out, snapping at the bird, which drops the
snake. You watch as the blood-red line plummets
to the ground, disappearing into the mass of the
fighting warriors.

This is clearly a sign from the gods.
◊ *If the gods are telling you to attack, go to 98.*
◊ *If the gods wish you to retreat, go to 24.*

You tell the messenger to pass the order to the
left and right wings, instructing them to turn
and attack the rear of the Persian central line. He
quickly disappears from your sight and you turn
your attention to the battle close at hand. The
Persians are still pushing your men back, and a
sense of desperation has started to fill the air.

You push your way to just behind the fighting men and urge them to hold on. You shout to them that help is coming from the wings. The Athenians hear your words and start to fight with renewed energy. For the first time in nearly an hour, your men are holding the Persians.

You sense the other Athenians are beginning to arrive. The Persians soon realise the situation is changing, and in fear of becoming trapped, they begin to fight like wild animals.

At first it seems your plan is working. It seems the gods are willing you to surround and destroy the Persian army, but it is not to be. Though it is now clear hundreds of Athenian warriors are joining the fight from the rear, the Persians have not been slow to react. Acting like a single creature, the Persian line is pulling away from your line. They are retreating; gambling that they can fight their way to the safety of their ships.

◊ *If you wish to follow the Persians and kill as many as possible before they escape, go to 68.*

◊ *If you wish to show mercy and let the Persians retreat, go to 51.*

---

28 You quickly realise that the Persian archers will do too much damage, and you issue the order for your men to sprint forward. The advance halts, whilst the word spread. Finally a toot of the horns

signals the charge to begin.

It starts at a jog, the sweat quickly forming as you move forward in the morning heat. Arrows thud into the ground around you and Athenian warriors begin to fall. You run and run, your heart thundering in your chest.

Then the front of the line hits the row of black-and-white Persian shields. The first rank of hoplites push into the enemy line. Screams of death and the clash of metal fill the air. Blood flows. The Persians drop back as they absorb your charging hoplites, who begin to calmly line up in the phalanx formation. The well-trained Athenians lock shields and create a wall. Then they push forward into battle.

You drop out of combat and move just behind the phalanx. Dead Athenians and Persians litter the ground.

◊ *To step forward and get involved in the battle, go to 97.*

◊ *To wait and see what happens, go to 48.*

You pass the order to follow the track that passes between the mountains and sea.

The track you follow is wide and easy to navigate. Your men are able to march side by side and progress at some speed. The sun is low in the sky but a cooling breeze from the sea make the heat bearable.

Soon you are within reach of Athens, and the sight of the city crouching in the hills spurs your men onwards. The last mile is made at a slow jog. Your joints scream in pain and sweat covers your body. Yet pride fills your heart and you keep pace with even the youngest warriors.

As you jog you glance to the bay below and see a number of Persian ships at anchor.

An hour later and you are able to form your men into a phalanx outside the gates of the city. As the sun begins to set nothing happens. The ships just sit. You wait. Then as the last rays of sun disappear, the ships pull up anchor and slow turn and crawl away.

Athens is safe… for now!

◊ *You have won the Battle of Marathon and defended Athens. Now turn to 93.*

You glance over at Leontis. His shield is raised and he moves in close to protect the right-hand side of your body. As you go to thank him you catch a glimpse of his lopsided smile.

You have only been in battle a few minutes and already you are breathing deeply. You wonder what a man of your age is doing risking his life.

Moments later the Persian line emits an ear-piercing shriek and springs forward. In a blur your men react, pushing back at them. A Persian in front of you raises his sword to strike, but Leontis steps in front of you, sticking the blade of his spear into the side of the exposed warrior.

A second later you are in danger again. A Persian confronts you. You block the initial thrust from his spear with your shield. You step backwards, edging your shield to the right and thrusting low with your spear. The Persian is quick and blocks the blow with his wicker shield. You kick out at the shield and it comes away from his hand and falls to the dusty ground. Panic flashes on his face. He is left unprotected and at your mercy.

◊ *If you wish to finish the Persian with a thrust to the head, go to 70.*

◊ *If you feel the body is the best target, go to 89.*

31 You have no choice but to keep fighting, but slowly
the phalanx ahead of you continues to retreat.
The Persians are pushing hard. Yet, the phalanx
is holding. It is moving backwards, but it is
remaining firm. Perhaps you can win? Perhaps the
Persians will tire? Perhaps warriors on the wings
will defeat the enemy and come to your aid?

As if to answer you, a stream of Persian
warriors rush in from the wings, many of them
dressed in unusual red and yellow gowns. At the
head of the wave are fleeing Athenian warriors.
These are being cut down even as you watch.

You think about turning and running. But
you realise your old legs will never outrun the
Persians. You even consider suicide, and throw
your spear and shield to the ground to draw your
sword. At that moment, you are ready to rip open
your own throat in a final, desperate act. Yet, you
realise you don't have the courage. Instead, you
throw your sword to the ground.

The Persian warriors are just a few paces away
now. You close your eyes and trust your fate to the
gods.

◊ *You have been defeated and the Battle of Marathon
is lost. Turn to 61 to discover your fate.*

Without hesitation you stride to the aid of the Polemarch. The Immortals see you and pull back slightly. Callimachus is pleased to see you.

Callimachus fights off two attackers, but a third has moved in behind him. Before you can shout a warning, the third Immortal attacks. He plunges his spear into the Polemarch's back, the mighty blow forcing the metal tip cleanly through his chest. All the Persians stop for a moment as the Polemarch glances down at the red spear tip. He drops his weapon then grasps the shaft in two hands, and with a mighty effort he pulls the spear through his own body. With triumph he throws the spear to the ground, before collapsing.

Four Immortals close in on you. You parry a blow, but are caught by the second thrust. A blow to your head sends you crashing to the ground. The final blow slices into your stomach and you slump to the ground, praying that the darkness will come.

◊ *You have been killed in battle. Turn to 64 to discover your fate.*

33 If you can inspire your men once, then you can surely do it twice. The phalanx has stopped pushing forward and has come to a stop. Once again you push your way in amongst your men and shout brave words. Yet, this time the reaction is different. Instead of them racing to their deaths, your men just look at you with anger. You move out of the ranks and wait just behind the phalanx.

As time passes, little changes. The hot sun still beats down, though a cool breeze wafts in off the sea. The centre remains locked with the Persians. One minute your men are giving ground, being pushed back a few paces. However, the next they are pushing forward and regaining the ground. Yet, your warriors continue to die. You have reached a stalemate.

◊ *If you wish to let the battle continue, go to 8.*
◊ *If you feel the battle is lost, and you want to save the lives of your men, go to 79.*

34 Your considerable experience in battle tells you that the phalanx will hold against the weaker Persians. So you wait, confident. As you watch you see the huge phalanx first give a little ground, but then hold. All along the line, as far as you can see, the Athenians stand eight deep. The front rank is engaged in combat, its shields locked with the Persians. However, it is the ranks behind that are doing the real damage, with their spears thrusting over the heads of the front rank, poking and stabbing at the Persians.

As you watch in silence, a few paces behind the mighty phalanx, a warrior staggers to your side. His shield shows he is from a tribe you instructed to fight on the right. His face is etched with worry and his armour and helmet are blood spattered.

"The right wing is in peril," he says panting. "The devils are too strong and we are already falling back." You ask about the left, but he is not sure. However, he thinks the situation may be the same.

What will do you?

◊ *If you wish to send warriors from the fight in the centre to help on the wing, go to 20.*

◊ *If you feel that by winning the battle in the centre you will be in a better position to help the wing, go to 88.*

35 Retreat is not an option. You wait just behind the phalanx, watching the mass of warriors push, stab and kill. You are filled with pride at the heroics and the knowledge that songs and stories will be written of this day pleases you.

But as time passes you can feel a change in the air. You start to see that to the far left and right, Athenians warriors are running back from the wings. The stream of men becomes a flood before your eyes. The wings must have broken. The central phalanx is now an island that is in danger of being flooded by Persians.

◊ *If you feel the battle is lost, go to 43.*
◊ *If you wish to fight on, go to 82.*

---

36 Suddenly the world feels a very dark place. You know the right and left wings are winning, but ahead all you see is defeat. Brave Athenian warriors are being cut down as you watch. Their screams fill your ears and their blood is splashed over your body and face. Though the Athenians hold their formation – shields locked, each man protecting his neighbour – they are being slowly pushed back. Time is running out…

You turn to your friend Leontis, wild fear in your eyes. You tell him to pass the order to retreat. You tell him now is the time to drop back, perhaps you can take flight to Athens and save the city?

Leontis smiles calmly, lifting his hand to your face. A calmness sweeps through your body.

"These men are brave," he says, "they would rather die here than run like scared dogs. Let them fight." You realise that he is right, the battle is not lost! Your moment of cowardice passes and you realise the battle may yet swing in your favour.
◊ *Go to 53.*

Stepping forward, you emerge from the relative safety of your ranks and confront the huge Persian. Your eyes come to his chest and you need to look up to the sky to see his face – he is smiling. In one hand he holds a huge wooden club, in the other a flashing blade. Dirty black-and-white material, which was once a uniform, hangs loosely off his body. The stink of his sweat is almost overwhelming.

You are lifting your spear in preparation to do battle, when the huge club swings through the air and slams into your helmet. The shock knocks you to the ground. The Persian steps over you, grins and starts to bring the huge club down to crush your skull.

Yet instead of sudden death, the club hangs motionless in mid-air. You let out a breath and look up to see blood spurting from an arrow embedded in the monster's throat. The Persian forgets about you and lets out a sickening gurgle.

Hands appear all around you and drag you from the ground to behind the phalanx. It takes you a few minutes to recover from your near death experience. Your joints ache and you have difficulty breathing in the heat, but you are alive. Despite your heroics the phalanx remains locked in stalemate.

◊ *If you have had enough, and feel that the battle cannot be won, go to 50.*

◊ *If you feel that the phalanx can still win the battle, go to 10.*

---

38 The lethal Persian arrows continue to rain down, killing brave Athenians. You feel you have no choice but to get your men out of danger. You try to turn to pass the order to retreat. However, as you stop marching the men to your left and right bump into you. You are causing chaos, and all around you hoplites are stumbling into each other. You have no choice but to keep moving forward, if only to stop the men around you tripping and falling to the floor.

As you push forward more arrows fall. The man to your right suddenly screams. You look over to see the man clutching his blood-soaked face. His helmet has been knocked off and the shaft of an arrow is sticking out of his eye. As you look, he slumps to the floor and is trampled by the advancing Athenians behind.

◊ *If you still wish to try to order the retreat, go to 67.*
◊ *If you wish to let the phalanx continue its advance, go to 11.*

The sun is already dipping low in the sky when you first get news of the Spartans arrival. The Spartan leader has ridden ahead and arrives on the battlefield before his army. You meet him on the plain where you explain that time is short and you must all march to save Athens now.

The Spartan leader is hesitant and explains that his men must first see the Persian dead. He says his men believe the Persians to be demons and that only by seeing their bleeding corpses will they go on to fight without fear. You agree and retire to your tent to wait.

The sun is setting when the Spartans are finally ready to leave. You pass the word for your army to prepare to march through the hills to Athens. You watch with pride as the mixture of Spartans and Athenians start the long slog towards Athens. Looking up to the horizon your heart sinks as you see a soft red glow in the early night sky. You have seen this before. It can only mean one thing – fire. You set off to Athens, knowing that you are already too late...

◊ *You have won the Battle of Marathon, but your victory is not complete. The city of Athens burns! Go to 64 to discover your fate.*

---

40 You scream the order to retreat. At first nothing happens; your men plod on, arrows falling. You keep screaming. One or two warriors turn and start to jog back, away from the arrows, then it is ten, then the whole centre of the army.

It takes just a few minutes for the men to retreat, but it takes longer for them to form back into a phalanx. You wait behind your men as they prepare themselves.

You pass the word to attack, but this time you order your men to run through the arrow cloud. The attack starts again, slowly at first, the hoplites holding their line. Then, as they near the Persians and the arrows begin to drop, the men pick up speed. You manage to keep up with them, but your chest pounds with the effort. You are now flying headlong, head down, praying to the gods that the arrows will miss you.

Then you crash into the Persian line. Their strange armour and colourful hats seem out of place. You stab and parry. First one Persian, then another, hits the dust. Your spear is tipped with their blood. After the initial impact, you see that your men have managed to form a strong line just in front of you. The Persians dropped back at first, but have now moved to meet your men.

◊ *To continue fighting with your warriors, go to 97.*
◊ *To step back and wait to see what happens, go to 48.*

41 You have practised attacking at a run, and you have heard tales of it being done in battle, but you have never actually seen it happen. You swallow hard and shout that on your command all men must charge forward. You wait for a moment while the order is passed along. Arrows continue to fall and screams ring out as brave men die.

Then – "RUN!"

The charge starts as a fast walk, then a run, and becomes a sprint. The hot sun brings sweat quickly to your body. The adrenalin flows as the wind rushes past before you finally thunder into the Persians.

The wicker-shield wall is pushed backwards. Your shield is up, spear down. A Persian stands in front of you. You stab at him, then you slash at another Persian. He ducks so you smash your shield into his face making him stagger backwards.

Then a few of the enemy manage to group together and form a wall, and this quickly becomes a line. Instinctively your hoplites do the same, reforming the phalanx. Within minutes the phalanx is pushed up against the Persian shield wall. Stabbing and slashing continues. You drop out of the combat to decide your next move.

◊ *If you wish to wait a moment and see what happens, go to 77.*

◊ *To push your way into the combat again, go to 44.*

Leontis fights like a demon. A block with his shield and a stab with his spear leaves one Persian dead. Yet the brave warrior stands little chance. He fights on but soon begins to tire. A Persian spear eventually passes his guard and pierces his neck. Leontis slumps to the floor.

Grief sweeps over your body and you feel your knees weaken. Then a shadow falls over you. A warrior stands in front of you; he is taller than you; in fact he is taller than any man you have known. His armour is golden and shimmers in the light. As you gaze upon his mighty features for a moment they flicker and change. His face transforms into that of boar, then back into that of a man again. But this is not a man. It is the god of war – Ares!

"Your cowardice will be punished by the gods," says Ares.

Then he is gone.

Your cowardice is clear to all about you and though the battle rages on, some warriors start to move in your direction. They are angry and disgusted with the shame you have brought them. They overwhelm you – death comes quickly. The gods have spoken.

◊ *You are a disgrace to Athens. Go to 61 to discover your fate.*

Even the wisest warriors know when a battle is lost and you pass the order to retreat. But even as the words leave your lips you know it is not possible. Instead, you take a few steps back and wait.

As you watch, the Athenian phalanx begins to disintegrate. Warriors peel away from the formation and run for their lives, rushing past, heading for the safety of Athens. Yet you remain, waiting.

At last you see the Persians head in your direction. You stand firm, shield raised and spear poised. At first the enemy seem reluctant to fight, and a growing crowd surrounds you. One Persian breaks from the ring to attack, but you stamp forward, thrusting your spear into his face.

Then a tall, noble Persian steps from the crowd. He looks you in the eye and drops to one knee – a sign of respect. He then stands and offers his outstretched hands. He is unarmed. You pause and then throw your shield and spear to the floor. Stepping forward you surrender to the general.

◊ *You have been defeated at the Battle of Marathon.*
Turn to 61 to discover what the gods have in store
for you.

Standing and watching is not your style. Pushing your way into the back of the phalanx, you soon wriggle towards the front ranks. Warriors part to let you pass and it is only moment before you can smell the sweat of the Persians. You have just settled into your position, feeling the ebb and flow of battle, when things change.

The Persians have decided to make a push just in front of where you are fighting. A huge Persian, at least a head taller than all around him, has appeared in the Persian line. He wears no helmet and a black bush of beard covers his scar-ridden face. He leads the attack, physically heaving your warriors out of his way. The men in front of you step backwards to avoid the giant. The warriors immediately in front of you shuffle backwards as a space appears around the monster of a Persian.

As you struggle to keep your balance in the tight scrum of Athenians, the warrior in front of you trips and slumps to the ground. He is alive but has rolled to the feet of the huge Persian. He now rests in the small pocket of space between the two lines. His death will come soon. Will you help the man?

◊ *If you wish to sprint forward and rescue the downed Athenian, go to 37.*

◊ *If you wish to stay in formation, but let the man die, go 58.*

You wait until the last possible moment, then drop your shoulder and roll to the left… The Persian, clad in black and white and carrying a wicker shield, anticipates your move and as you hit the floor you see the point of the spear following your movement. You try to lift your shield to block the thrust but you are too slow.

The blade enters your body in your lower back and pain fills you. You try to move, to wriggle free but it is too late. For a second you are filled with energy and start to lift yourself off the ground. Your shield is gone and your spear is lying flat under your body. You move to recover your spear and collapse. Unable to gather the energy to move, you lay in the blood-soaked earth, awaiting the darkness of death.

◊ *You have been killed in battle. Go to 61 to discover what the gods have in store for you.*

46 You pass the order for your men to take the mountain pass. Your warriors are quick to organise themselves, since you are all aware of the danger faced by Athens. Within an hour you are on the dusty path that cuts over the top ridge of the mountain. The track snakes up the side of the mountain, the steep path makes walking difficult and your old joints ache. The heat is almost unbearable despite the late hour and a cool breeze from the sea.

It is not long before your progress slows as the army struggles to navigate the narrow dusty track.

The sun is setting when you finally catch a glimpse of Athens. Ahead, in the gloom of the early night sky, you can see the outline of your city. Your heart misses a beat as you realise that it is framed by orange flames. You are too late to save your people…

◊ *You have won the Battle of Marathon, but your victory is not complete. The city of Athens burns! Go to 64 to discover your fate.*

47 It seems your plan to place the strongest troops on the wings has pleased the gods. The messenger informs you that on both the left and right the Persians are starting to retreat. He says that on the right the enemy are streaming away and racing for the safety of their ships, whilst on the left the Persians are fleeing into the marshes, where many are drowning. Yet, the battle is far from won. The battle in the centre has not been going as well as you would have wished, and the strong Persian

army continues to push your men back. The Athenian line in the centre is holding for now, but it won't be long before it crumbles and the Persians break through. You must now decide how to make the most of this advantage.

◊ *If you wish to order the men on the wings to return to your position and strengthen the attack in the centre, go to 71.*

◊ *If you wish to order the wings to attack the Persian centre from behind, go to 27.*

48 You watch in quiet fascination as your warriors clash with the Persians. Your men are better armed than the Persians and probably better fighters, but there are more Persian warriors. In places you see your men being pushed back.

You notice that ahead of you the Athenian hoplites have dropped back, and a space has formed between the two armies. In the space you see a huge Athenian warrior. As he fights, his bronze armour flashes in the sunlight. Sweat drips from his muscular arms and legs. Around him are four Persians, they have him trapped like a wild boar. You realise it is your friend Leontis – a tribe leader.

No Athenian warrior dare break the line to help and you watch in horror as Leontis parries with his shield and probes with his spear. He is holding out now, but they will overwhelm and destroy him soon.

◊ *If you wish to risk your life to try to save your friend, go to 86.*

◊ *If you wish to wait and let your friend be slaughtered, go to 42.*

49 You scream for your men to keep in their phalanx formation. Your booming voice reminds them that they are Athenians who are not scared of the pinpricks of the Persian arrows. Yet, even as you speak the words, a man in front of you is struck down by several arrows.

The advance is slow as the phalanx tries to stride forward. Each man walks while remaining in a line, his shield protecting the man to his right, while deadly arrows thud home from above.

You soon realise the advance is stopping. You look up and to your horror you see that the Persian line is still some way ahead.

◊ *If you wish to order your men to drop back out of range of the arrows, go to 40.*

◊ *If you wish to keep going in formation, go to 18.*

50 You scream out the order to retreat. You tell your men to return to the safety of the camp to fight another day.

Your words are like a disease that spreads through the ranks, poisoning all who hear them. Within just a few minutes the retreat begins. At first it is orderly, with the back ranks taking a few paces backwards and moving away from the fight. Then the panic starts as the front ranks realise that they have no support. Persian warriors rush forward and begin the slaughter.

You are no hero, and you throw down your shield, turn your back and run. But the years have caught up with you, and the Persians soon surround you, hacking you down like the coward you are.

◊ *You have been killed in battle. Go to 61 to discover your fate.*

Though the battle has been short, it has been bloody and you feel that it would be foolish to test the gods' patience. You shout for your men to let the Persians flee.

The Athenian line comes to a halt, shields still linked, the sun flashing on the weapons and bronze armour. The Persians retreat slowly. They seem wary; worried that you may be playing a trick. They leave a line of Persian warriors facing you, ready for battle. Behind this line you can see the rest of the enemy rushing to the ships.

It takes a couple of hours for the Persian warriors to board their ships. Unhindered, the Persians set sail off the beaches. You are left watching – hoping – that they will return home, rather than carry along the coast towards Athens. Your last act of the day is to order a sacrifice of a thousand goats, just to keep the gods happy!

◊ *You have defeated the Persians at the Battle of Marathon, but your victory is not complete. Go to 13.*

52 You turn to Leontis and gesture for him to follow you. He looks confused, but as you move backwards pushing through your own men he follows.

There is a crack of thunder, and suddenly the world around you vanishes. Where the battle raged, it is now silent. Leontis and all your hoplites have disappeared, along with the Persians. Instead a huge warrior stands in front of you on the plains of Marathon. He is at least three metres tall. His armour is golden and his hair blond, but his eyes are wild with rage.

"To retreat now would mean death," thunders his voice, though his lips do not move. "The gods demand you fight on."

Slowly, the sound of the battle floods back into your ears. Your men are back and the screams of dying men surround you. Leontis is by your side; he looks concerned. You are about to speak when another man appears in the distance. You recognise him as one of the messengers from the right wing.

◊ *Retreat is no longer an option, so go to 95.*

53 You know that with men on the left and right winning, you just need to hold on…

Your hoplites are formed up in the phalanx formation with the front rank pressed shield to shield. The men behind are pushing against their backs, trying to hold the Persian advance. As they try to stand firm, spears are thrust through the gaps; poking and cutting. The Persians fight in a similar way. Their large black-and-white wicker shields are strong and can turn away a spear. It has become a deadly game of push and shove.

◊ *If you believe that the larger Persian army will win and that you should retreat while you can, go to 81.*

◊ *To push into the battle and inspire your men to fight, go to 16.*

54

You pass the order to prepare for battle. The dusty plain stretches out ahead of you with tufts of rough green fennel bushes sprouting from the dry cracked mud. On the left are marshes and hills, on the right is the calm blue sea.

The Athenian army is split into ten tribes, each with about 1,000 trained hoplites. However, your force is boosted by 1,000 brave Plataean fighters, who have come with their leader Arimnestos to fight the Persians. In total you command about 11,000 warriors.

You have decided to keep the centre of your army strong and assign three tribes to fight in the middle. Your tribe is one, but the tribes of Leontis and Antiochis will fight alongside you. You have known these men for many years and trust them with your life.

On the right you place the Polemarch Callimachus with his tribe, plus three others. He will position his men between you and the sea. On the left are the Plataeans with the remaining Athenian tribes. Here they will be protected by the marshes and hills. You pause a moment considering who will command this wing. By rights it should be an Athenian, but the Plataeans' leader, Arimnestos, has impressed you. You decide to give the command to the young man.

It is tradition that the hoplite phalanx should

fight with eight ranks of men, but this will bring a problem. By using eight ranks your army will be too narrow and the Persians will overlap. But with a strong centre you have no option but to fight in eight ranks.

◊ *Now go to 6 as your mighty Athenian army moves into position…*

You stop just short of the ships and watch the slaughter in safety. It is difficult to guess how many Persian bodies you can see on the beach and in the surf, but it must be at least one hundred. In places the sea washes red with blood.

Most of the Persian ships have escaped and are out in the bay. However, a few ships remain. The Persians that have not yet escaped fight desperately to reach them.

You pass word to a nearby warrior to return to camp and bring burning torches. After a few minutes, a group of camp followers bring the torches down to the beach.

You pass the order to burn the ships. Within minutes the burning torches are being thrown onto the remaining few ships. Some fires are put out, but others blaze through the ships as the wood catches alight. Persians jump desperately from the burning wrecks, only to be slaughtered by merciless Athenian blades and spears.

An hour later, the fighting is over. The Persian ships have either escaped or sit burning in the surf. You now return to the tents in the olive grove to consider your next move.

◊ *Go to 69.*

With a rush of courage you force your way from the line and into the gap between the armies. Three Persians see you and race to do battle. You drop your left shoulder, bringing up your shield to eye level.

One warrior, dressed in the black and white of the Persian spear men, is shocked by your sudden aggression, and before he can react you brush him aside with your shield. The force of the blow knocks him backwards and you plunge your spear into his belly.

The second Persian is a few paces ahead of you, with his spear already levelled in your direction. Without stopping you flip your spear so its weight rests in the palm of your hand and then launch it through the air towards the man. It wobbles, but its flight is true, striking the man just below the chin, embedding the metal tip deep into his neck.

Then there is the third Persian. With a fluid motion you draw your sword. The Persian twists, trying to bring up his shield to protect his body. You rock on your back foot, blocking his black-and-white wicker shield with your own round bronze shield. You step inside his guard and thrust your blade through his stomach up into his chest. His body stiffens and you feel the warm breath leave his lips.

Your charge has taken you away from your line

and you are now dangerously close to the Persians. A wall of black-and-white shields is within touching distance! You swiftly collect your spear, but what should you do now?

◊ *If you wish to wait for your warriors to come to your aid, go to 75.*

◊ *If you feel now is the time to step back to your line, go to 14.*

57 You thrust your spear downwards at the unsuspecting Persian, plunging it into his soft flesh. The Persian screams and you whip out the spear as he slumps to the ground – dead.

The next man you reach is also running, his back exposed. This time you don't hesitate and aim higher, thrusting your blood-covered spear through his chest. The man turns his head to look at you – he is just a youngster. You feel his ribs split as he twists away, so you pull your spear free, leaving him sprawling behind you in the blood-soaked sand.

You are now at the beach. Ahead of you is a thin line of Persian warriors, dressed in yellow and purple. These are the Immortal guards and they seem to be protecting the Persians behind them as they board their ships.

To the right, you catch a glimpse of the unmistakable form of Callimachus, the spiritual leader of your army. He has been surrounded by a party of the Immortal guards. His shield and spear are raised to protect himself, but the Immortals pace about him, waiting. His life hangs in the balance.

◊ *If you wish to risk you own life to try to save Callimachus, go to 32.*

◊ *If you wish to preserve your life and attack the Persians on the beach, go to 87.*

58 As commander, your life is far more important than a hoplite and you resist the temptation to prove your bravery. Instead, you remain in position and start shouting orders. You demand that the line reforms. Your words seem to have power, and the warriors around you burst into action. As they move to form a line you lose sight of the huge Persian and the warrior at his feet.

Once again you are just a few ranks behind the fighting. At first you can feel the line being pushed back, a pace at a time. But for each pace you lose, the phalanx rallies and pushes back, regaining the ground. Occasionally, an arrow zips over your head or a Persian spear is thrust forward and deflected by your helmet.

Minutes pass and it is clear that the battle is once again in stalemate.

◊ *If you feel that the gods do not want you to win this battle, go to 50.*

◊ *If you feel that the phalanx is on the verge of breaking the Persian line, go to 10.*

59 You inform Leontis that you fear for the safety of Athens. He agrees, explaining that he too is worried about an attack on the city.

Despite the urgency, it takes over an hour for the army to prepare itself for the slog through the hills to the city. You order your men to set off at a jog, but you grow increasingly tired with every passing minute.

The pace slows as hoplites clog the narrow, hilly paths. When you do finally catch sight of Athens, the scene fills you with horror. Across the valley you can see Persian ships anchored in the harbour. The city of Athens, perched high up in the hills, is ablaze; smoke bellowing into the evening sky. Outside the mighty city you see masses of warriors, dressed in colourful uniforms.

You are too late! The attack on Marathon was a diversion. Whilst your men fought and died, the Persians attacked Athens. You watch on helplessly as the city crumbles and burns.

◊ *You have won the Battle of Marathon, but your victory is not complete. Go to 64 to discover your fate.*

Your men are elated at the retreat of the Persians, and many begin to follow the fleeing enemy. You scream out the order for them to halt. You spot Leontis to your right, organising a small group of Athenian warriors, and jog to his side. Here you pass the order for the men to let the Persians flee.

At first Leontis is reluctant, but you explain that the gods wish for the fighting to stop. He is loyal, and instead of questioning you, he orders the men to let the Persians go.

As you watch, you see the Persians collect on the beach by their ships. Time passes and as it becomes clear you are not pursuing them, they begin the long job of boarding their ships and escaping to sea.

The sun now hangs low in the sky and you have retired to the shadows of the olive grove. Your armour has been removed and you have been refreshed by a wash in the cool sea. Leontis approaches you and then asks of your plans.

◊ *If you wish to wait for the Spartan army to arrive before returning to Athens with a combined force, go to 39.*

◊ *If you feel you need to march to Athens in case the Persians sail along the coast and attack, go to 59.*

Rating: Poor General

You are a poor general and your lack of honour in battle angers the gods.

It seems that you are not cut out to be either an ancient Athenian warrior or general. You made the wrong decisions, ignored good advice and were unlucky. The battlefield of Marathon is a deadly place and you need to be ruthless and decisive if you are to survive.

◊ *Now go back to section 1 and try again…*

You feel that if you can break out into the hills then your men have the best chance of escape. You pass the order and set off at a jog. Now that you are free of the phalanx you can move quickly. Ahead of you the ground changes from the dusty plain to a lush green paradise.

You lead your men past the pockets of battling warriors and into the high grass. The going is hard. The ground is marshy and each step forces mud and oozing water into your sandals. Added to that streams crisscross your path, causing you to lose your way.

Suddenly, a group of Persian warriors emerges from the grass ahead of you. They are dressed in the yellow and purple of the Immortals. You call your men to you, but they have become scattered. You take a couple of steps backwards to find a better footing, but your wet sandals slip and slide.

Then an Immortal is upon you. You twist to strike him, but you lose your footing and tumble backwards into the muddy water. Brown water covers your face and body. You thrash about trying to regain your feet, but your heavy armour pulls you down. You need to breathe... you open your mouth and water floods in. As the water fills your lungs you stop struggling and drift off into the darkness.

◊ *You have died in battle. Go to 61 to discover your fate.*

---

63 The fighting around the ships is desperate. In places, the sea has been turned red with blood. As you work your way to the water's edge, you have to tread carefully to avoid bloody corpses, severed limbs and spilled entrails.

The Persians are trying to board the few ships that have not yet escaped. The fighting is close and you throw away your spear, and draw your sword. A Persian jumps up and grasps the hull of a ship that is slowly backing away from the shore. He holds on and tries to pull himself up. You step forward and the water comes up to your knees. The man starts to thrash and kick his legs. With a couple of quick jabs from your sword, you stab the man twice and he drops into the surf.

To your left you see a face you recognise.
It is Cynegirus, the brother of the playwright
Aeschylus. Cynegirus has grabbed the stern of the
escaping Persian ship. The enemy on board scream
and spit, until suddenly an axe blade appears
from the chaos of the ship. It thunders down onto
Cynegirus's exposed arm. He lets out a scream
as his hand is severed. He drops into the sea in a
fountain of blood.

An hour of carnage passes before the last of the
ships escape. The battle is over, but the sun is low
in the sky. You return to the tents in the olive grove
to consider the next move.

◊ *Go to 69.*

Rating: Good General

64

Well done! You have proved yourself to be a good
Athenian general.

You have a firm grasp of what it would be like
on the battlefield at Marathon. You are able to
make good choices and can be ruthless when it is
needed. Perhaps you lack a bit of luck.

However, in 490 BCE Miltiades commanded his
men to victory on the battlefield of Marathon, *and*
prevented the Persians entering the city of Athens.

◊ *Now go back to section 1 to try again. This time pray*
the gods are on your side (a goat sacrifice at an
Athenian temple might help).

65 Despite the enemy pressing from all sides, you fight on. Hoisting up your spear, you face the nearest Persian. He is a small man who cowers behind his wicker shield. You face him squarely, dodging to the left and right before thrusting out with your spear. The point catches his arm causing the man to scream with pain and drop to the floor.

Before you can react, Leontis is at your side with his sword ready. He stands over the Persian on the ground and grabs his collar. The first blow removes the Persian's head, which bobbles away along the blood-soaked earth. Leontis then slices at the man's limbs. Finally, Leontis rests his foot onto the torso of the body and rolls it into the crowd of advancing Persians.

The Persians are stunned by the violence and their advance pauses. Leontis grabs your arm and pulls you away from the enemy, dragging you back through your own men to safety.

You turn to confront him, but before you speak you see a messenger approaching through the crowd.

◊ *Go to 95.*

66 You glance at Leontis and smile; he nods in your direction and you turn to face the masses. They seem confused by your bravery and hold back.

Then you see why the Persians have not closed in. Dodging behind their line is a small Persian dressed in red with a yellow cap. In his hands is a small bow. He ducks from man to man using the cover of the black-and-white shields. You watch as he works his way along the line and appears just ahead of you. He draws his bow and shoots an arrow right at you.

Suddenly everything around you seems to move in slow motion. Despite your age, your instincts take over and you force your body to the right. The arrow flies past and you hear a scream from behind.

Leontis taps you on the shoulder and you glance over. A messenger from one of the other tribes is calling your name. You signal for Leontis to follow you behind the Athenian line.

◊ *Go to 95.*

---

67 The phalanx continues its advance, with Athenians dropping all around you under the rain of Persian arrows. The enemy remains some distance ahead and you feel that you must take action before it is too late.

Swinging around, you again scream for the

retreat. This time the men around you slow down before they slam into you. But you are in the centre, and those hoplites further away on the left and right continue to advance.

The phalanx eventually slows and stops as the order is passed along. The Persians sense the moment and suddenly a huge wave of arrows darkens the sky. As the arrows start to strike home you feel panic rise amongst your men. Screams ring out. A man behind you is hit and his blood splashes onto you. Then you too are hit – an arrow piercing through your thigh muscle. You shriek out as the pain washes over you and your leg buckles. You lie on the ground as the sky darkens once again. This time it is not Persian arrows that cause it, but the life drifting from your body.

◊ *You have died in battle. Go to 61 to discover your fate.*

68 The Persians know the battle has turned – you can see panic on their faces. They know they are about to be surrounded and the only chance they have is to retreat – but you have other plans.

You command your men to attack. A huge roar erupts from your line as the Athenians surge forward in a wave. The Persians panic; many turn to run, breaking their line. The battle quickly breaks down into a mass of individual scraps.

You rush into the confusion and quickly become engrossed in the lust to kill, cutting down Persian warriors as they run. All around you Persian bodies litter the blood-soaked earth.

You push your way through the crowd when you hear a shout above the din. To your right you see an Athenian warrior in trouble – it's the Polemarch Callimachus! A large group of Persian warriors, dressed in the shocking bright yellow and purple gowns of the feared Immortal guards, have gathered. They circle around the Polemarch like hungry mountain lions, waiting for the moment to strike.

◊ *If you think you can help Callimachus, go to 17.*
◊ *If you think it is better to fight your way to the beaches and stop the Persians escaping, go to 23.*

The heat of the day is starting to fade when you arrive at your tent. You call a servant to bring a bowl of cool water, and when it arrives you wash your face and arms. The water turns a murky red as the blood and dust mix together.

You leave the tent and stand quietly as you consider the next move. Earlier in the day, the Persian cavalry escaped by ships. This had been the spark that had convinced you to attack. However, you now wonder why these troops ran away. Were they planning to sail around the coast and attack Athens?

It is clear that you must return to Athens and protect the city from any Persian attack. However, you are expecting the Spartan army to arrive on the battlefield at any moment.

◊ *If you wish to wait for the Spartans before marching to Athens, go to 39.*

◊ *If you feel you have no time to lose and wish to march immediately to Athens, go to 92.*

70 Your ageing muscles force the tip of your spear forwards at the Persian's head. He ducks out of the way and you strike him with your shield. He falls backwards into the dust. You strike him with your spear again, this time pinning him to the earth. He struggles briefly, then stops. As you look away from the dead man's face you suddenly realise that there is only you and Leontis facing the enemy. All around you the Persians have pushed back the Athenians, and you risk being cut off and captured or killed.

◊ *If you wish to play it safe and drop back the few paces to your line, go to 52.*

◊ *If you feel it would not be heroic to retreat, go to 66.*

---

71 You know that if you order an attack on the rear of the Persians, it will trap them. You also know that trapped men will fight like wild boars, so you pass the word for the warriors to come to you.

It is not long before you see Athenian warriors appearing in broken groups of three and four. You instruct them to join the line of hoplites in the centre. Leontis moves to your side. You are pleased to see the mighty warrior and give him the task of directing the reinforcements.

With each new warrior, the Athenian phalanx gains more strength. The Persians are struggling

to maintain their forward motion. You watch
with pride as the phalanx holds, and then begins
to push back the Persians. Yet the Persians also
remain in a solid line, their black-and-white wicker
shields protecting the spear men behind.

The battle has reached a turning point.

◊ *If you wish to order your men to charge forward to
try to break the Persian line, go to 83.*

◊ *If you wish to wait to see what happens in the next
few minutes, go to 21.*

72 As the messenger approaches you turn your back, making it clear you have no desire to speak to him. The messenger ignores your rude behaviour and instead strides around to stand in front of you.

"I have important news," he says.

◊ *Go to 47.*

---

73 Freed of the restrictive phalanx formation, you and your men are able to move quickly. You pass the order to head for the groves and set off at a jog. Ahead of you is open plain and it does not take long to reach them. You pause to assess the situation. The sun is hanging low in the sky but the heat of the day is still intense. Your old body is aching and pain flashes periodically from your old war wound on your left elbow.

As you wait, more Athenians appear around you and after about thirty minutes you have collected a crowd of warriors. However, the news is not good. With each man that appears the picture gets worse. It appears the wings have collapsed and the central phalanx is only just hanging on.

You decide to act and order your men back to Athens. The battle here is lost...

◊ *You have been defeated at the Battle of Marathon. Go to 61 to discover what fate the gods have in store for you.*

You watch with growing horror as it becomes clear the Persian line is gaining some momentum. Your Athenian warriors continue to fight, but they can't halt the Persians, and the Athenian line continues to be pushed back.

As you watch the line, a warrior suddenly trips and falls. He tumbles to the ground and is suddenly surrounded by Persian warriors as the Athenians continue to be pushed back around him.

For a moment he is left alone between the two lines. Then, as he tries to regain his feet he is attacked. He remains on the ground, defending himself with his shield.

◊ *To rush forward to try to help the man, go to 9.*
◊ *If you think it would be too dangerous, go to 3.*

75 Pride is a dangerous thing and rather than retreat you choose to stay and fight. The Persians ahead of you pause at first, waiting for you to run. However, when they see you intend to try to defeat them on your own they push forward. You are quickly surrounded by Persians. You twist and turn, knocking away their sword blows and spear thrusts with your shield.

Then a sword blade slices through your right arm, causing you to drop your spear. The Persians show no mercy as you are struck with spear after spear, until your old legs finally collapse under you. For a moment all is peaceful, then, nothing...

◊ *You have died in battle. Go to 61 to discover your fate.*

As you watch the battle slog on, a sickness rises within you. The heat is stifling. You can hardly breathe so you rip off your helmet.

Suddenly all is very clear… The battle is lost! Your men are dying. Panic builds, your head throbs. Finally you throw your shield and spear down and wave your arms high in the air. You scream "RETREAT! RETREAT!" as you dash up and down behind the phalanx. But your men don't move.

Through the heat you see a small group of hoplites heading towards you. Their faces look angry and concerned. You rush over to them, pleading with them to retreat. The men speak to you, but the noise in your head is too loud, and you can't hear what they say. Something about "cool" and "tent". "Shade" is another word that you just make out. Your sword is taken and you are firmly led away to the tents in the olive grove.

Your madness has ended the battle for you.

◊ *You will play no further part in the battle. Go to 61 to discover your fate.*

You know from experience that fighting in a phalanx – in the hot sun – is exhausting. But you also know that you must make the right choice.

The front rank of your phalanx is pushed up tightly to the front rank of the Persian army. Spears from both sides poke, stab and slash over the heads of the front ranks and into the warriors behind. As brave Athenians fall, a warrior from behind steps over his body, ready to do battle in his place.

As you watch you see your men sometimes give ground – falling back a few paces – then at other times push forward, regaining the ground. It is not clear who will win.

◊ *If you feel this battle can't be won, go to 50.*

◊ *If you wish to get involved to try to turn the battle, go to 44.*

As the confusion of the battle subsides your thoughts return to Athens. Though you have defeated the Persians on land, you suddenly realise that their ships could at this very moment be sailing along the coast to attack Athens. You call to your commanders to gather together all the men they can and within an hour you set off towards Athens.

The journey is painful in the hot afternoon sun. You follow the dry, dusty path along the coast and through the foothills south of Athens. You try to encourage your men to march faster, but they are tired and injured from battle.

When you finally catch a glimpse of Athens the evening light is fading. You feel your heart sink to the pit of your stomach as you first spot the unmistakable black shapes of hundreds of ships moored on the beach. Looking east to the city you see flames licking the sky all about the houses and temples. The horizon glows orange.

You are too late and the battle at Marathon was nothing more than a diversion. Tears fill your eyes as you think of the carnage and slaughter that awaits you in Athens.

◊ *You have won the Battle of Marathon, but your victory is not complete. The city of Athens has fallen to the Persian invaders. Go to 13 to discover your fate.*

79 You can see no other option than to order a retreat and get your men out of danger so they can fight again later. You push close to the back ranks of the phalanx and calmly pass the word to retreat.

To begin with just the men closest pull back. However, as the word spreads, panic slowly builds. Soon warriors all around you are retreating; moving away from the phalanx and weakening the front ranks.

As a result, the men in contact with the Persians no longer have the strength of men behind them, and they are unable to hold back the enemy. Gaps appear as the front line breaks and your men tumble to the floor. Persians flood through the gaps and the killing starts.

You stand like a rock in a river as your men flood past you. You lift your shield and prepare your spear, but you never get a chance to use them. As the retreat turns to a rout you are knocked backwards by your own men. You try to regain your balance but you are knocked again – this time you fall to your knees. You try to rise but an Athenian knee catches you in the face, causing your nose to crack. You hit the floor, blood leaking from your broken nose. You are kicked, trampled and stamped by hundreds of Athenian feet.

◊ *You have died in battle. Go to 61 to discover your fate.*

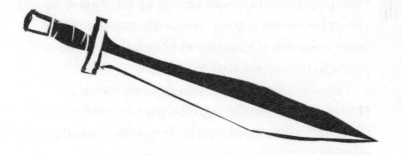

You watch as the sun rises over the hills and light fills the valley where the Persian army is preparing for the day ahead. It soon becomes clear that they have no intention of attacking. Instead they remain at the far end of the valley. You look out across the sea to your right-hand side, where Persian ships sit at anchor, waiting for their men.

You are proud to be leading the Athenians. They are a good people and you wish to prove that you are a worthy warrior... Your thoughts are broken by the appearance of Callimachus, who strides from the trees behind you.

"Miltiades, the other commanders are becoming restless. They fear that by doing nothing we leave Athens unprotected. They want to attack now."

◊ *If you wish to prepare to attack the Persians, go to 90.*

◊ *If you think the Persians will soon attack and wish to wait, go to 84.*

81 You pace forward, shouting wildly for your men to retreat before it is too late. Some men just stand and look back at you, others keep fighting, but enough pause and start to fall back.

The Persians sense the change and surge forward, pushing through the gaps in the Athenian line. Men rush about you, at first Athenians, but then Persians.

You keep shouting for the retreat. Suddenly a Persian confronts you; a twisted smile on his bearded face. His body makes an easy target and you aim your spear for the killing blow. With all you weight you thrust the point of the weapon forward.

But you are too slow…

The Persian anticipates the thrust and rolls his body to the left. The point of the spear misses his body, flashes past him and embeds into the soft soil. You are unbalanced and the Persian shoves you to the ground.

He thrusts his spear down through your shoulder, pinning you to the ground. Then he draws a long, curved sword. You bring up your hands to protect your face, but you are helpless. His laughing face is the last thing you see.

◊ *You have died in battle. Go to 61 to discover your fate.*

You have been a warrior all your life and fighting is all you have ever known. Sealing your fate, you push into the mass of Athenian warriors ahead of you. Yet, even as you join the phalanx, you sense it is too late. You warriors are weak and tired, and the tight block is starting to break up. Gaps are appearing all around you, and Persians are starting to push into the first couple of ranks.

Suddenly you are faced by a small Persian. His face is smooth and his hair is plaited, so that for a moment you think he is girl. Athenian warriors are packed closely to your left and right and wielding your spear is difficult. The Persian facing you is armed with a sword. You thrust your spear forward, but he dodges it easily, stepping under the shaft. You try to bring your shield around to protect your stomach but the man to your left is blocking you.

The Persian steps forward and plunges his blade into your stomach. You splutter blood and stagger backwards. He turns to strike another Athenian before you hit the dust.

◊ *You are dead. Turn to 61 to discover what fate the gods have in store for you.*

You know that the battlefield is no place for a weak leader. You decide that now is the time to prove you are a great Athenian, whose name will live for ever in legend.

An old war wound on your left arm forces you to readjust your heavy shield. In your right hand sits your well-balanced spear. You push yourself to the front of the phalanx. The tight ranks of men part to let you through. As you emerge from the front rank, the Persians are just paces away. You scream for your men to follow you.

The Persian ranks part slightly as you race forward and within seconds you are amongst their men. A black-and-white-clad Persian, armed with just a curved sword, stands in your way. He draws back his arm and swings the sword towards your neck. You duck, feeling the blade slice over your head. A cloud of purple horse hair floats down around you. The Persian has sliced the plume clean from your helmet! You thrust upwards with your spear, catching him in the stomach.

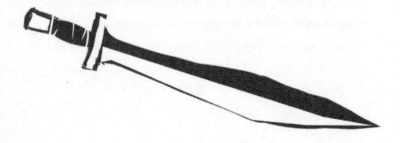

Despite your heroics, the battle is still not won. Your warriors have followed your charge, but within a few minutes the Persians have dropped back a few paces and re-formed their lines. Once again your phalanx, and their steady black-and-white line, face each other.

◊ *If you wish catch your breath before deciding the next move, go to 26.*

◊ *If you feel the battle is lost and the Persians can't be defeated, go to 94.*

Despite the early hour the sun is already hot and your warriors soon become restless.

Time passes and the sun creeps higher in the sky, yet still the Persians wait. Finally, Callimachus comes to you once again. He looks old in the heat of the day, sweat beading on his brow.

"Miltiades, this is no good. We must act now. I don't care what our rules say, today we risk Athens. What your enemies say is true, you are a Persian at heart! You are removed. Return now to Athens."

You start to argue but it is clear the decision has been made. With great sadness you collect your belongings and return in disgrace along the coast road to Athens.

◊ *You will play no further part in the battle. Go to 61 to discover your fate.*

You pass the order prepare for battle. You know the Persians will wait until you are ready to fight; in their own way they are – sometimes – honourable people.

Your army is split into ten tribes, each with about 1,000 warriors. You also have the help of 1,000 brave Plataean warriors, led by Arimnestos, a young commander with a passion and intelligence that clearly burns brightly in his eyes. In total you command about 11,000 warriors.

As you organise your men you look out across the plain to see the Persians already moving into position.

It is Athenian tradition that the Polemarch commands the right wing. So, you ask Callimachus to take four tribes, including his own, and position them on the right with their flank protected by the beach.

You order your tribe, plus two others, to position themselves in the centre. You will command these three tribes directly. Yet, you will not be alone, tribe leaders Leontis and Antiochis are brave men who will help when needed.

It is normal for your hoplite phalanx to fight with eight ranks of men, but this will bring a problem. If you do use eight ranks for all tribes, then your army will be too narrow and the Persians will overlap. You have no option but to weaken the centre and order your phalanx to fight with just four ranks. It is better to be weak, than to allow the Persians to get around the back of your army.

Finally you send the remaining four tribes, including the Plataeans, out to the left. Here they will be protected, on one side by the marshes and hills. You ponder for a moment who to place in command of the left wing. You instincts tell you that it should be an Athenian warrior but the young Plataean, Arimnestos, has impressed you. You decide he should command the left wing.

◊ *Your mighty Athenian army is ready for battle!*
  Go to 15.

You would rather die at the hands of the Persians, than let a friend die helplessly. You reposition your shield, adjust your spear so it sits firmly in your hand and rush forward to save Leontis.

As you charge from the crowd, anger flashing in your eyes, the four Persians pause. The Persian closest to you is an easy target, and you run your spear through his chest. Leontis seizes his moment. He lifts his spear before throwing it at the Persian standing closest. The spear strikes his chest and knocks him to the ground.

The Persian nearest to you edges forward, his black-and-white shield angled to protect his body. You shift your weight and lunge your spear towards the man's unprotected head. He is slow to react and the point of your weapon pierces the man's temple. You feel the crunch of bone and the man crashes into the dust.

Leontis glances in your direction and you see that his blue eyes are alive with energy. You take two steps in his direction; protecting him with your shield. The final Persian slowly backs away, hiding behind his wicker shield. Moments later he disappears into the Persian line.

A small space has formed between the two armies, with Leontis and yourself positioned in the middle. The blood-soaked earth at your feet is littered with Athenian and Persian bodies.

Then the Persian line pushes forward again.

◊ *Go to 30.*

Your heart is heavy as you turn away from Callimachus. You are sure that helping him would have been suicide, but as you stride away you can't shake the feeling that you are a coward.

You head towards the ships. As you approach, a scene of carnage meets your eyes. The Immortal guards, who were protecting the Persians by the ships, have been pushed back close to the shore. Persian warriors and Athenians are intermingled where the sand and sea meet. The Persians are desperately trying to drag themselves onto the remaining ships. At the same time, Athenians stalk about stabbing and slashing at them.

◊ *To get involved with the fight on the shore, go to 63.*
◊ *To watch from a distance, go to 55.*

It is tempting for you to weaken your centre and send troops to help on the wings. However, you feel that your only chance is to defeat the Persians here and now, and then go to the aid of the other Athenians. You turn to the warrior and explain that the left and right wings have no choice but to fight on. He listens in silence and then jogs away.

You push your way into the back ranks of the phalanx. Warriors push, slash, thrust, poke and spear. Amongst this noise and confusion you raise your spear above your head and shout that this is a day they can prove themselves before their gods. You scream, "Today you are born as true warriors! Dying for Athens is a joyful and noble act. Men not here today will be jealous that they never had the chance to be heroes. My promise to every one of you is that all who fight here today will forever be your brothers. Songs and stories will be written of your sacrifice!"

At first it seems your words have no effect, but then – slowly – the phalanx pushes forward. Cries rise up from along the line as they keep pushing. You slip out of the ranks of men and to your amazement see that the block of warriors has pushed back the Persian line at least five paces.

◊ *To urge your men to even greater feats of courage, go to 33.*

◊ *To pause to see what happens, go to 5.*

89 You seize the moment and show the Persian no mercy. Stepping forward onto your front foot you ram your spear into the stomach of your enemy. You are surprised that there is little resistance from the man's flesh and bone. Your spear passes with ease through the Persian, the point emerging from his back.

The man stands, his arms outstretched, his gaze looking to your spear in horror. You move your weight onto your back foot and slip the blood-soaked spear from his body. It is now greasy to touch.

The Persian has sunk to his knees and his hands cover the small puncture wound that spurts blood. As you admire your work you suddenly become aware that you are in danger. Leontis remains at your side but the Persian line has pushed forward. You are confronted by a wall of black-and-white shields – you must react now to avoid being surrounded.

◊ *If you wish to order your men to retreat, go to 52.*
◊ *If you wish to stand your ground and keep fighting, go to 65.*

You give the order to prepare to attack. You know
the Persians better than any Athenian alive. You
have lived with them, even fought with them. You
know how they think and you know how to kill
them. You know they are arrogant and you know
they will never stop – ever!

Now is the time to prove you are a mighty
Athenian warrior! Now is the time to show the
Persians that Miltiades is a god amongst men!

You look out at the battlefield. To the right
stretches the yellow sand of the beach. The Persian
ships are anchored further down the coast. The
plain of Marathon in front of your men is flat and
dusty, and covered only by small fennel bushes. To
the left the ground becomes more uneven as the
plain turns firstly to a marshy area and then into a
rocky slope.

You know that the Persians will have their best trained and most heavily armed warriors in the centre of their army. They always do.

As your men begin to line up, you have two options. You can either put your best hoplites on the left and right wings of your army. This would give you a chance to overwhelm the weaker Persian flanks, but your centre would be weak and vulnerable. Or, you could make the centre of your army strong and match the Persians. This would leave your wings weaker, but they would be facing weaker Persians.

◊ *If you wish to make the wings strong, go to 85.*
◊ *If you wish to make the centre strong, go to 54.*

To be in the front line again feels good. Images of historic battles and moments of great honour flood into your head. You look left and right to see the line holding and you feel confident.

The battle continues to rage. Persians appear in front of you, testing the wall with their attacks, but it holds firm. You fight on, feeling like a teenager again. You thrust and stab with your spear, blocking and dealing death to any Persian foolish enough to come within range.

In the gaps between attacks you look about, trying to see what is happening elsewhere on the plain, but you can see no further than a few paces before the crowd of warriors blocks your vision.

Time passes and eventually you hear your name being called. You slip from the line, letting it form up around your position and move backwards. A messenger is waiting for you.

◊ *Go to 47.*

---

92 Time is of the essence, and you quickly pass the word for all able warriors to prepare themselves to march to Athens. It is late afternoon, and a calmness has returned to the battlefield.

Finally, around 1,000 men are ready to race to prtoect Athens.

◊ *To follow the mountain path, which is the shortest route, but narrow and difficult to move freely along, go to 46.*

◊ *To follow the pass between the mountain and the sea, which is longer, but wider and easier to move along, go to 29.*

---

93 Rating: Great General

It is clear that you were born about 2,500 years too late! You are a genuinely talented general who understands how to lead warriors and win battles. You are ruthless, make great choices and have the luck of the gods.

◊ *Now go to section 99 and find out what really happened at the Battle of Marathon.*

Pushing into the back ranks you scream that the battle is lost, that the Persians are too strong. Your men trust you, many have even fought alongside you on past campaigns. Hearing your words causes them to falter. Just seconds pass before a number of men are pulling away from combat. You keep screaming for retreat and more men follow.

Then the flood begins… Panic rips through the ranks and men all around you turn and run. The speed of the change catches you unawares and all of a sudden you are isolated. The Persians have pushed forward as the phalanx collapsed and you have been caught by this wave.

The man that kills you is young. You turn to see the Persian, his teenage looks are only slightly masked by a poor attempt at a beard. The inexperienced warrior lowers his spear as he passes you, plunging the blade into your side. You wince as it hits, breath exploding from your lungs. You are spun to the floor. At first you think it is nothing. But as you try and stand, strength escapes you. You look down to see a red river of blood gushing from the wound.

◊ *You have died in battle. Turn to 13 to discover your fate.*

You and Leontis move through the line to meet the messenger; the bull image on his shield shows you he is one of the Plataeans from the right wing. The hot sun is now high in the sky. You lean on your spear, and lower your shield to the ground. Your old war wound screams with pain as if to remind you that you are too old for this young man's game.

The messenger tells you that the Plataeans are close to breaking the Persians on the right wing. The news is welcome. You smile and pat the messenger on the shoulder, before sending him off.

You pick up your shield and look along the Athenian line. In the distance the right wing has pushed on past your position. Glancing to the marshes on your left, the situation is the same, with the left wing further ahead than your men.

However, your hoplites in the centre are only four deep, and they are outnumbered by the Persians. No matter how well they fight they are losing ground. It is just a matter of time before the Persians overwhelm your men. Your Athenians will hold out for as long as possible, but you don't know if this will be long enough for the warriors on the left and right to be victorious.

◊ *If you feel the battle is lost and wish to order the retreat, go to 36.*

◊ *If courage and pride are too important, and you wish to keep fighting, go to 53.*

You wait until the last possible moment, then drop your shoulder and roll to the right… The Persian fails to anticipate your move and as you hit the ground you see the point of his spear bury itself into the dusty soil.

You get to your feet – your shield is gone, but your spear is ready. The Persian is off balance and you quickly stab the spear into his side. Before he can react, you pull out the spear and stab him again. He slumps down and you don't wait to see if he is dead, instead you grab your shield and move quickly back to the centre of the phalanx.

As you arrive you are met by a warrior carrying a sword and shield. The shield markings show he is from a tribe you ordered to fight on the left wing. He is covered in splatters of blood and a large cut on his arm is crusted with dirt. His feet and legs are covered in dried mud.

"The wings are in retreat," he says panting heavily. "The Persians have pushed us back. They will be here soon!"

You order the man away.

◊ *If you wish to order your men to retreat before they are overwhelmed by enemy coming from the wings, go to 22.*

◊ *If you feel your best chance is still to win in the centre, go to 35.*

You feel the blood running hot in your body as you step forward to do battle. Ahead of you is a mass of hoplites; their shields locked, their spears thrusting at the Persians. The enemy faces you, their black-and-white shields protecting their bodies as they too thrust with their spears.

You push through the line of hoplites and as you emerge, the Persians drop back slightly, surprised by your bravery.

A Persian warrior breaks free from the line in front. Suddenly he is close, a twisted smile on his brown, bearded face. You bend your legs slightly, readying yourself for his attack. But before he can move, you drop your left shoulder, driving your shield against his. You catch the stench of his sweat as the man is caught off balance and staggers backwards. You bring your spear around from the right and over your shield. You tense your arm and stab swiftly into the man's neck. The tip of your spear pierces his throat, before you strike again at his body. The man falls down dead at your feet.

From behind you a huge, god-like warrior emerges from the crowd. His bronze armour glints in the sunlight and his sculptured muscles tense and twist as he positions himself next to you. You look across and smile at your friend, Leontis.

◊ *Go to 30.*

The omen is clear. You are the soaring eagle and the Persians are the blood-red snake. The gods have shown that it pleases them for you to win this battle.

With renewed hope you pass out a message for Leontis to come to you. When he finally appears, you tell him of the omen and he agrees that it is indeed a sign from the gods.

Together you move amongst your men, telling them of the omen and showing how the gods wish them to be victorious. Within minutes your men are fighting with renewed energy. The whole of your front line is now engaged with the Persians. Your men's spear thrusts have more power and slowly, ever so slowly, the Athenians begin to push back the Persians.

As the battle begins to turn in your favour, the Persian warriors who are not engaged start to move back towards their ships on the beach. At first it is just a few warriors, but this trickle becomes a stream, then a flood.

Panic spreads through the Persian ranks as if a floodgate has opened. Hundreds panic, trying to back away from your hoplites and run for their lives.

◊ To let the Persians flee, go to 60.

◊ To order the Athenians to chase down the Persians like dogs, go to 7.

What actually happened on that summer's day in 490 BCE is a mystery. There are no written records, and the best "evidence" comes from a Greek historian called Herodotus. He wrote a huge book called *The Histories*, which contained a chapter about Marathon. When historians look at this book some of what Herodotus wrote is very accurate, some of it is factually wrong and some – well – he just made up!

However, here are some of the things that we are pretty sure are true:

◊ Archaeology and ancient monuments mean that we are confident that the battle was fought on a plain of Marathon with the sea to one side and marshes on the other.

◊ Ancient historians (not Herodotus) suggest about 10,000 Greeks fought at the Battle of Marathon. The size of the Persian army is harder to guess. Ancient historians say somewhere between 100,000 and 200,000 warriors, but modern historians think that it was more likely to be about 25,000 Persians.

As for the events of the day, here is what historians think happened:
◊ The Greeks had a weak centre and strong wings
◊ The Athenian warriors did attack at a run to avoid the arrows
◊ The strong Greek wings beat the weaker Persian wings
◊ The Persian centre collapsed
◊ The Persians tried to escape on their ships
◊ Many Persian ships were set on fire

Even as the afternoon sun sinks in the sky, the heat is still hot. You remove your helmet before picking your way back through the dead bodies of brave Athenian and Persian warriors. The dusty, fennel-covered ground is deep red in places, with blood oozing across your path.

By the time you return to the olive grove you are exhausted and numb. Your first act is to find a priest and order him to set about recording the number of dead. You tell him that Athens must sacrifice a goat for each man that has been killed. You hope this will be enough to appease the gods.

You remove your armour and wander to a clear part of the seashore to clean your face and body. The cold sea is soothing, and you crouch in the water for a number of minutes scrubbing at your hands. Soon a messenger jogs down to you. He informs you that the Spartans have arrived, and also that the Polemarch is nowhere to be found.

You return to the grove to greet the Spartan general but inform him, with sadness, that he is too late. With ceremony he asks permission for his troops to examine the bodies of the Persians. You agree, knowing that for many Spartan warriors this will be the first time they will have set eyes on the exotic warriors from the south. You suspect it will not be their last.

As the sun finally sets, the blue sky darkens as the last light of the day disappears. You turn to face the direction of Athens where you see a soft orange glow on the horizon. You have seen this kind of thing before, and it can mean only one thing – fire! Athens is burning!

◊ *You have won the Battle of Marathon, but your victory is not complete. The city of Athens has been sacked by the Persians. Go to 13 to discover your fate.*

BATTLE BOOKS
BEHIND THE SCENES

The author: GARY SMAILES

I decided to write the Battle Books series after becoming really annoyed that someone had not already got off their backsides and written them for me. You see, battles are just so great to read about – all the weapons and action – in fact, I don't understand why there aren't more books about them…

I live on the Wirral, which many years ago was inhabited by real-life Vikings. Sometimes, when I'm writing and I get stuck, I go out for a walk with my (stinky) dog. I imagine I'm part of a Viking army defending my land.

If I could have three wishes, one would be that I was a Viking, and the other would be to own a Viking longboat. The third would be that my dog didn't smell so much!

The artist: OLLIE CUTHBERTSON

Hi, I'm Ollie and I drew the artwork in *Battle Books: Marathon*. I love capturing the action in a battle. Sometimes it could just be a single brave hoplite, other times it could be a whole scene including Athenians and Persians, like this artwork.

I draw in two main stages for Battle Books. First I create a rough sketch, then I make changes and draw the final piece in ink, with some grey fill.

ROUGH

This piece is from paragraph 3. I focused on the Persian archer to begin with, but then I thought that you don't want to necessarily see him straight away. So in the final version I pulled back the viewpoint to include more of the scene. Now the archer is harder to spot – just as he would be during the real battle.

FINAL

BATTLE BOOKS

Take up your weapons and prepare to fight your own battle...

978 1 4451 0112 5

978 1 4451 0113 2

978 1 4451 0114 9

978 1 4451 0115 6